TURNER & ARCHITECTURE

cover
**Durham Cathedral Looking East
along the South Aisle** 1797–8
(cat.no.14)

ISBN 0 946590 91 5
Published by order of the Trustees 1988
for the exhibition of 28 March – 10 July 1988
Copyright © 1988 The Tate Gallery All rights reserved
Catalogue written by Ian Warrell and Diane Perkins
Designed and published by Tate Gallery Publications,
Millbank, London SW1P 4RG
Printed by Lund Humphries

Sponsored by

Chartered Surveyors

TURNER & ARCHITECTURE

THE TATE GALLERY

Foreword

This exhibition concentrates on Turner's lifelong involvement with architecture, a subject that has been relatively neglected despite its importance both in his art and in his personal life. Turner's virtuoso drawings of picturesque buildings are famous, but many people will perhaps be surprised to discover that he was also the designer of his own house and picture gallery; and that he once said if he could begin life again he would rather be an architect than a painter.

Turner and Architecture continues our series of small displays of Turner's watercolours, drawings and sketchbooks, drawn from the riches of the artist's Bequest to the nation. It has been selected and catalogued by Ian Warrell and Diane Perkins of the Turner Collection staff. They would like to extend their thanks to all those who have helped in preparing the exhibition, especially Professor and Mrs Harold Livermore, and Maurice Davies who provided information on Turner's Perspective Lectures from his as yet unpublished researches.

The exhibition and catalogue have been sponsored by Drivers Jonas, who have recently been appointed surveyors to the Tate Gallery. We are most grateful to them for their generous support.

Alan Bowness *Director*

Turner and Architecture

Architecture is a pervasive theme of Turner's life and art. Although he did not consider himself an architect, his work invariably bears the stamp of a mind trained in the technicalities of the architectural profession.

Before he was fourteen he was employed in making elevations of buildings for architects such as Thomas Hardwick (1752–1829). A more enduring influence was the work of the architectural draughtsman Thomas Malton (1748–1804). Along with Thomas Girtin, Turner attended Malton's classes on perspective in Long Acre, Covent Garden. The meticulously-observed topographical studies made by Malton depict buildings with a directness and clarity that the young Turner was quick to emulate.

The watercolours and sketchbooks of Turner's early career testify to his considerable competence as a draughtsman, whether his subject was the carved intricacies of Gothic architecture, Picturesque ruins, or the public buildings of London. He was also commissioned to paint the country houses of his patrons, and although he never failed to record the details of his subject with accuracy and precision, he developed the narrow topographical tradition of this genre to embrace his wider interests as a landscape painter. Although architecture tended to be absorbed by this increasing preoccupation with landscape, he made it one of the six categories into which he analysed the range of his art in his ambitious publication, the *Liber Studiorum*. The didacticism which led him to undertake this work was given a further channel for expression when he was elected to the post of Professor of Perspective at the Royal Academy, where he gave his first lecture when he was thirty-six. The post had evolved largely as a means of inculcating the skills of perspective drawing into architectural students at the Academy Schools. Turner drew his own illustrations, and although his topic was nominally perspective, the content of the lectures proved to be more wide ranging and quite often of an explicitly architectural nature.

In addition to painstaking preparations for his own lectures, Turner helped Sir John Soane with the diagrams for his lectures as Professor of Architecture. His friendship with the architect was long-lasting and Turner's designs for his own country villa, Sandycombe Lodge, owe much to Soane's influence. In the course of his career he designed several other buildings; these are dealt with in a separate section. He was familiar with the work of other celebrated architects of his day such as James Wyatt, Charles Barry and John Nash, at whose home on the Isle of Wight he stayed in 1827.

Turner's career as an architectural draughtsman received constant stimulus from his many sketching tours abroad. These gave him the opportunity to study at first-hand styles of architecture he had only encountered in the drawings of other artists. In particular the buildings of Classical antiquity in Rome fired his imagination, whilst the architectural riches of Venice were a source of constant pleasure. The sketchbooks Turner filled on his travels provided material for many of his published engravings, such as his *Annual Tours* of the Loire and Seine. Other drawings executed for engraving projects, most notably the vignettes for Samuel Rogers's *Italy*, were recognised in their time by Walter Scott as 'beautiful specimens of architecture'.[1]

On a much larger scale, paintings like 'Forum Romanum' (Gallery 104), for all their grandeur, treat architecture with vivid immediacy, drawing on the careful sketches made in his notebooks, some of which are exhibited here. Another painting, 'Ancient Rome: Agrippina landing with the Ashes of Germanicus', is reminiscent of the architectural fantasies of Soane and his pupil Michael Gandy; Turner recreates from his imagination the buildings of the Classical past while always convincing us of his firm understanding of the 'bricks and mortar' of architecture. The professional grounding he had received as a youth remained of practical importance to him throughout his life.

---

[1] Gerald Finley, *Landscapes of Memory: Turner as an Illustrator to Scott*, 1980, p.72

Measurements are given in millimetres followed by inches in brackets; height precedes width

1 **Wanstead New Church** 1789–90
pencil 217 × 320 (8½ × 12½)
Turner Bequest; IV A
D00051

An important early architectural connection for Turner seems to have been Thomas Hardwick (1752–1829). Hardwick lived in Brentford and Turner may have been introduced to him there when staying with his uncle. Hardwick also worked in the 1790s on repairs to St Paul's, Covent Garden, the church in which Turner had been christened close to where his family lived in Maiden Lane. While still in his early teens, Turner spent some time in Hardwick's office washing-in colour grounds and making elevations of the buildings Hardwick was involved with. Work on the church shown here, St Mary the Virgin, Wanstead (or Wanstead New Church) commenced in 1787 and the building was consecrated three years later in June 1790. Turner was presumably acquainted with Hardwick before work on the church began, for as well as a watercolour based on this squared elevation, he made a watercolour of Old Wanstead Church for the architect's collection.

2 **Radley Hall from the South** 1789
pen and ink and watercolour 330 × 510 (13 × 20)
Turner Bequest; III D
D00049

This view is one of a pair of finished watercolours based on sketches made in one of Turner's earliest sketchbooks (the *Oxford* sketchbook, T.B. II). Turner's work for Thomas Hardwick involved making drawings of the buildings on which the architect was working, showing them in a landscape setting. This drawing clearly shows Turner's style as an architectural view-maker at this time.

Turner's early method was closely related to architectural conventions. Simplified washes are used as a means of modelling the building in sunlight and Turner has blacked out the windows according to traditional practice. In later architectural views, he is credited with the innovation

of depicting the effect of reflected light on window panes, something which apparently led to his break with the architect William Porden, (1755–1822), another early employer.

3

3 **Bristol Cathedral from the North-West** 1791
pen and ink and watercolour 340 × 312 (13⅜ × 12¼)
Turner Bequest; VII A
D00108

By the end of 1789 Turner was working with the architectural draughtsman, Thomas Malton whose precise draughtsmanship he quickly learnt to master. The clear recording and observation of architectural details are combined here with a suggestion of drama in the steeply rising perspective resulting from a deliberately low viewpoint, another feature that he probably borrowed from Malton.

He visited Bristol for the first time in 1791, staying with John Narraway, a friend of his father, sketching buildings that were of particular topographical or historical interest. The sketches made in the *Bristol and Malmesbury* sketchbook and associated watercolours such as this and 'Bath Abbey' (T.B.VII F) show Turner's preoccupation with Gothic architecture, true to the taste of the time.

4 Petworth Church from the North West 1792–4
pencil and blue wash 272 × 214 ($10\frac{3}{4}$ × $8\frac{3}{8}$)
Turner Bequest; XXIII E
D00379

Turner has followed the traditional architectural practice of indicating areas of light and shade with grey washes, a method he perhaps learnt from his teacher Thomas Malton (1748–1804). Turner made several drawings and paintings at the Petworth home of his patron, the Third Earl of Egremont, including some of the interior of the church. This watercolour shows the entrance to Lord Egremont's family gallery. The spire visible in the top right-hand corner was removed in 1800 and replaced almost thirty years later by a spire designed by Sir Charles Barry.

5 Temple of Vesta, Rome *c.*1795–7
pencil with grey and blue watercolour wash
240 × 328 ($9\frac{1}{2}$ × 13)
Turner Bequest; CCCLXXV 10
D36531

In the mid 1790s Turner was employed by Dr. Thomas Monro to make copies of the drawings in his collection. Turner worked with his talented contemporary Thomas Girtin, who reportedly 'drew the outlines and Turner washed in the effects'.

This drawing, a collaborative effort by the two young artists, is a copy after John Robert Cozens who had travelled widely in both Italy and Switzerland. Cozens's drawings introduced Turner to the architecture and scenery of Europe and until he gained first-hand knowledge of classical architecture when he went to Italy in 1819, he was frequently to copy from the architectural diagrams or paintings of other artists.

6 The Pantheon, Oxford Street, the Morning after the Fire 1792
pencil and watercolour 516 × 640
($20\frac{1}{4}$ × $25\frac{1}{4}$)
Turner Bequest; IX A
D00121

The Pantheon, a London assembly hall, had been converted to a theatre in a new-Classical style in 1772 by the prolific architect James Wyatt. Large-ly constructed of wood, the building with its great dome burnt down almost overnight in January 1792.

This ambitious watercolour, which Turner sent to the Royal Academy exhibition later that year, records the aftermath of the fire which he had witnessed. Turner's interest was no doubt heightened by his involvement as a scene painter at the theatre. The fully formed and accomplished style of architectural topography which Turner had learnt from Malton has now taken on a greater breadth of ideas than is apparent in Malton's work. The sensitively observed effects of light on the building, the introduction of figures and the change in scale to a much larger water-colour are all indicative of Turner's growing confidence as a draughtsman.

7 Ely Cathedral: the Interior of the Octagon 1794
pencil 782 × 593 ($30\frac{3}{4}$ × $23\frac{3}{8}$)
Turner Bequest; XXII P
D00369

This large pencil drawing was made on a visit to Ely in 1794 and used as the basis for two finished watercolours exhibited at the Royal Academy. Much of the early material in the Turner Bequest consists of precise drawings of ecclesiastical architecture using this kind of pencil work derived from the drawing style of Canaletto: a complex web of dots, dashes and elegant curls defining the details of carved bosses and filigree masonry.

Turner deploys here his considerable skills as a perspective draughtsman, following the soaring lines of the building upwards to the heights of the octagon, thereby recreating the Sublime power of this extraordinary achievement of Gothic invention. The lantern over the crossing of the church had undergone some restoration in the mid eighteenth century by James Essex, and was later altered by George Gilbert Scott to what he felt was a more authentic style. The figures, especially those leaning over the balcony (which was removed during the later renovations), reinforce the towering grandeur of the whole design.

8 A Cathedral Porch 1794
pencil and watercolour 270 × 196
($10\frac{5}{8} × 7\frac{3}{4}$)
Turner Bequest; XXII E
D00358

This study seems to depict the Galilee Porch of
Ely Cathedral. The entrance here appears to
have been bricked up, possibly to prevent damage
to the structure during the eighteenth century
when Gothic architecture was unfashionable.
Tobias Smollett wrote in 1770 that cathedral
architecture was 'displeasing to the eye of every
man who has any idea of propriety and propor-
tion'. By Turner's day, subjects such as this had
become highly popular as Picturesque views, and
Turner recorded many cathedrals and abbeys for
use in later commissioned pictures. The figures,
lightly penciled in, merely provide a sense of scale
for the tall double arcading above them, whilst
Turner concentrates on the effect of light and
shadow on the stonework.

9 Salisbury Cathedral from the East
  c.1798
  pencil and watercolour 280 × 230 (11 × 9)
  Turner Bequest; XXVII G
  D00668

Turner was commissioned to make several architectural elevations of Salisbury Cathedral for
the Wiltshire landowner and antiquarian, Sir
Richard Colt Hoare. In this view the Lady
Chapel is seen below the pinnacles of the main
east end. The famous spire of Salisbury seems
rather stunted here, quite unlike the exaggerated
outline Turner made in his *Salisbury* sketchbook
(T.B. XLIX-6a, 7). As in the drawing of 'Ely
Cathedral', this watercolour demonstrates the
complex pencil draughtsmanship Turner prac-
tised as part of his topographical training.

10 Old Building with a Sluice 1794
  pencil with watercolour and bodycolour
  352 × 277 ($13\frac{7}{8} × 10\frac{7}{8}$)
  Turner Bequest; XXVII V
  D00683

In this unfinished architectural study, perhaps of
a mill converted from a monastic building,
Turner has made a pencil outline of a suitably

Picturesque subject and begun to wash in the
details of architecture, seemingly delighting in
the variety of stonework, especially the chequered
pattern of brick and knappered flint at the bottom
of the building.

**11 London: York House Watergate,
  Westminster with the York Buildings
  Waterworks** 1794–5
  pencil and watercolour 298 × 419
  ($11\frac{3}{4} × 16\frac{1}{2}$)
  Turner Bequest; XXVII W
  D00684

Turner's early appreciation of architecture was
marked by a firmness and precision of drawing
and a fresh sense of artistic licence, with towers
and spires rising above surrounding buildings to
provide a dramatic effect.

This drawing shows Turner's wide-ranging
tastes in architectural styles and is concerned with
the buildings of the commercial and industrial
London.

The plain wooden tower of the waterworks in
York Buildings is juxtaposed with the elaborate
baroque water-gate of Old York House, built in
1626 by Nicholas Stone, which can still be seen on
the Embankment. The group of buildings had
been drawn from the same angle by Canaletto
during the construction of Westminster Bridge in
c.1747.

12 Tintern Abbey 1794
  pencil and watercolour 358 × 225 (14 × $8\frac{7}{8}$)
  Turner Bequest; XXIII A
  D00374

The practice of architectural topography developed rapidly towards the end of the eighteenth
century through the increased output of publications of British and foreign guide-books catering
for the needs of a growing number of travellers.

Tintern Abbey had been illustrated in William
Gilpin's *Wye Tour*, a standard guide-book published in 1783 and this 'inchanting piece of
scenery' would therefore have been an appropri-
ate place for Turner to visit when he travelled to
Wales in the early 1790s.

The need to express space and evoke scale is
rendered by the adoption of a low viewpoint, a

device borrowed from Malton; but the subdued colouring and the delicacy of the brush-work are more closely connected with the manner of the picturesque and antiquarian topographers Edward Dayes and Thomas Hearne. This was obviously a popular subject for Turner since he painted several versions of Tintern Abbey around this time, one of which was exhibited at the Royal Academy in 1794.

13 London Bridge, with the Monument and the Church of St Magnus King and Martyr 1794-5
pencil and watercolour 342 × 217 (13½ × 8½)
Turner Bequest; XXVIII K
D00696

Although Turner was a Londoner, he made surprisingly few finished watercolours of London buildings, preferring to concentrate on the sites of antiquarian and picturesque interest in the provinces. The Old London Bridge, however, was a subject that he was to draw many times throughout his life, particularly in the early 1820s when he made many studies in the *Old London Bridge* and *London Bridge and Portsmouth* sketchbooks.

This drawing, based on a pencil study (T.B. XXVIII J) has a remarkably similar composition to other related subjects produced at the same time, notably Magdalen Tower and Bridge, Oxford in the British Museum.

14 Durham Cathedral Looking East along the South Aisle 1797-8
pencil, watercolour and bodycolour
758 × 580 (29⅞ × 22⅞)
Turner Bequest; XXXVI G
D01101

A sketchbook used on Turner's 1797 tour of the North of England (T.B. XXXV), contains several drawings made in Durham Cathedral, looking along the south aisle both to the east and to the west. This beautiful watercolour is based on p.12 of the sketchbook. Above the tomb of Bishop Nevill, the levels of clerestory and triforium arches are visible high over the heavy nave pillars, whilst the chevron-carved arches soar up out of sight. A screen across the entrance to the choir, which

Turner includes in the sketchbook drawing, has been omitted to allow a dramatic burst of sunlight in the south aisle, an effect which heightens the contrasts of light and shade.

15 A Capriccio with the Dome of St Peter's seen though a ruined Triumphal Arch
*c.*1797 or later
watercolour and bodycolour 436 × 580 (17⅛ × 22⅞)
Turner Bequest; CCCLXXX 18
D36667

The bright colours in this drawing, although similar to those used in some of the perspective diagrams such as 'Pulteney Bridge' (cat.no.20), have the air of such Italian 'vedutisti' as Carlo Labruzzi and this drawing may be a deliberate pastiche by Turner of such neo-classical continental souvenir-painters.

The delicately observed distant buildings are similar to Turner's copies after John Robert Cozens made in the mid 1790s (see 'The Temple of Vesta', cat.no.5). However, the arch appears to be an imaginary one, more neo-Classical than Roman, and perhaps relates to Turner's perspective drawings of *c.*1810. This sheet may well have been used as an illustration for one of Turner's lectures on perspective.

Architecture in Turner's *Liber Studiorum*

The *Liber Studiorum* was a collection of prints designed to illustrate Turner's range as a landscape artist. He was involved in the project from 1807 to about 1819, making sepia drawings for most of the subjects, from which etched outlines were derived to form the basis of the published mezzotints. He divided his material into six categories including Architecture. The other categories were Marine, Mountainous, Historical, Pastoral and Elevated Pastoral. His decision to include Architecture may have been influenced by the candidacy of Sir John Soane's pupil, Michael Gandy, for the post of Professor of Perspective at the Royal Academy, a position Turner coveted, and was finally elected to late in 1807. The Architectural category was to form a consistent part of the project, with a total of eleven engraved subjects, although it was omitted from three of the fourteen editions of the publication.

16

16 **Holy Island Cathedral; Lindisfarne** *c.*1807
pen and ink with sepia wash 183 × 262
($7\frac{1}{4}$ × $10\frac{3}{8}$)
Turner Bequest; CXVI N
D08115

This drawing was made for the second edition of the *Liber Studiorum*, published on 20 February 1808. Turner first made drawings of this subject on a visit to Lindisfarne in 1797. The *North of England* sketchbook (T.B.XXXIV, cat.no.51) contains several drawings of the ruined Priory church including that on p.54, which shows a similar view through the Norman arches. This book also provided drawings of Dunstanborough Castle, a subject Turner included as part of the Architectural category in the next instalment of the *Liber Studiorum*. The Lindisfarne subject shown here, however, is more typical of the Architectural category, and other ruined abbey churches, Kirkstall, Rivaulx and Dunblane, appeared in subsequent parts of the series.

17 **Morpeth** *c.*1808
pen and ink with sepia wash 186 × 260
($7\frac{3}{8}$ × $10\frac{1}{4}$)
Turner Bequest; CXVI Y
D08126

'Morpeth' seems a puzzling subject to include amongst a group of more obviously architectural drawings. As in two other subjects engraved for the Architectural category of the *Liber Studiorum*, 'Lauffenburg' and 'Ville de Thun', Turner focuses on no particular building, instead depicting a general townscape. His attention in the 'Morpeth' drawing falls on the building activity on the right-hand side of the picture. Watercolours throughout his career demonstrate that this sort of drawing was important as a means of utilising his skill as an architectural draughtsman.

18 **London, from Greenwich** 1811
mezzotint; 1st state 178 × 265 (7 × $10\frac{1}{2}$)
A00963

This mezzotint is based on the painting 'London', 1809 (Gallery 108). The mezzotint was published in the fifth section of the *Liber Studiorum* in January 1811. In the painting Turner barely defines the spire of the church on the extreme left. However, in this mezzotint he has broadened and considerably refined this detail, whilst also condensing Inigo Jones's Queen's House and the Royal Naval Hospital into a more solid mass. The spire of Nicholas Hawksmoor's church, St Anne's, Limeshouse, can also be seen on the right. Away in the distance is the dome of St Paul's Cathedral, which, like the Greenwich Hospital, was built by Sir Christopher Wren.

A vantage point much favoured by topographical draughtsmen, the view was already threatened in Turner's time by the advance of commerce. Turner notes in the caption to the painting the way the 'spires pierce the doubtful air, / As gleams of hope amidst a world of care'.

19 **Interior of a Church** 1819
mezzotint; 1st state 177 × 270 (7 × 10⅝)
A01052

Unlike the other *Liber Studiorum* subjects exhibited here, this mezzotint appears to have no preparatory sepia drawing. It does, however, relate to a group of drawings of church interiors in the *Wilson* sketchbook (T.B. XXXVII-26/27, 32/33), and to an oil painting now on display in the Reserve Galleries: the 'Interior of a Gothic Church' of 1797. This mezzotint is taken from the same viewpoint as the picture, but introduces additional architectural features such as the balustrade in the right-hand corner and the transverse arches beyond those in the immediate foreground. Although no location has been identified for any of these subjects it is possible that they depict the interiors of churches in the east of London, for other pages in the *Wilson* sketchbook show scenery around Greenwich.

Turner's Illustrations for the Perspective Lectures

In 1807, Turner was elected as Professor of Perspective at the Royal Academy. His first course of lectures did not begin until 1811 and the course was given sporadically until 1828, Turner finally resigning office in 1837.

Although these were public lectures, the course on Perspective had been established chiefly with architectural students in mind. Turner's accomplishment in perspective drawing, acquired during his early training as an architectural topographer, made him well suited for the post of Professor of Perspective.

The elaborate and carefully thought-out notes for the lectures, mostly now in the British Library, show how conscientious Turner had been in preparing these lectures; he had read widely and constantly revised them for each course. His subject-matter was wide-ranging, covering aesthetic theory as well as practical instruction; the lectures were criticised as a result as being 'more for the Professors of Painting and Architecture, the word "Perspective" hardly mentioned'.[1]

They were accompanied by illustrations, often of great beauty. There are over 180 perspective drawings in the Turner Bequest which vary from illustrative line diagrams, often derived from earlier academic treatises on Perspective such as those by Thomas Malton, Brooke Taylor or Joshua Kirby, to detailed watercolours of which these architectural views are examples.

Despite criticisms of the lectures as largely inaudible, incoherent or simply irrelevant, some attended them purely to see these illustrations. Thomas Stothard, a fellow artist who was completely deaf remarked, 'There is so much to see at Turner's lectures – much that I delight in though I cannot hear him'.[2]

[1] W.T. Whitley, 'Turner as a lecturer', *Burlington Magazine* XXII, 1912
[2] Andrew Wilton, *Turner in his time*, 1987

20 **Pulteney Bridge, Bath** *c.*1810
pencil and watercolour 672 × 999
(26½ × 39⅜)
Turner Bequest; CXCV 114
D17084

Turner often used examples of well-known modern buildings to illustrate his lectures. The lecture on practical perspective in the first series of 1811, contained illustrations of the Palladian Pulteney Bridge, Bath, built in 1750.

Turner showed his skill in perspective by the use of three successive studies of this building, describing the transition from a flat geometric diagram towards this finished perspective view.

21 **The Interior of Brocklesby Mausoleum**
c.1810
pencil and watercolour 640 × 490
(25⅛ × 19¼)
Turner Bequest; CXCV 130
D17101

This view of the interior of Brocklesby Mausoleum derives from sketches that Turner had made in 1797 at the seat of his patron the Earl of Yarborough. Like the 'Pantheon, Oxford Street' (cat.no.6), this building of 1792 was the work of James Wyatt.

Turner's lectures included discussions on aerial perspective, the changes in light and colour of receding objects, as well as linear perspective for which this seems to have been an illustration.

This drawing demonstrates the effect on the changing colours of light seen through the stained-glass oculus of the Mausoleum and shows how the use of shadows can give depth to a picture.

22 **Corinthian Capital** c.1810
watercolour and chalk 674 × 1010
(26½ × 39¾)
Turner Bequest; CXCV 103
D17073

This detail of a Corinthian capital was discussed in the lecture on practical perspective along with the illustration of 'Pulteney Bridge' (cat.no.20), and was worked up in a similar way from pencil diagrams to this finished perspective drawing. Turner described it as 'the beautiful Corinthian but the most difficult to put perspectively true'.

23 **The Spire of St George's, Bloomsbury**
c.1810
pencil and watercolour 742 × 467
(29¼ × 18⅜)
Turner Bequest; CXCV 145
D17116

St George's Bloomsbury, designed by Nicholas Hawksmoor, was twice used by Turner as an illustration for his lectures.

Turner is again dealing with fundamental problems not directly connected with perspective in its narrowest sense, such as the development of habits of perception and the relationship, often contradictory, of vision and measurable truth. This illustration is concerned with the way the eye foreshortens the tower and 'bends' the straight lines of the spire. Turner also discussed the statue of George II on the top of the spire and how its proportions are specifically designed to be seen from a distance.

24

24 **The Facade of Carlton House** c.1810
pen and ink and watercolour 684 × 1392
(27 × 54⅞)
Turner Bequest; CXCV 148
D17119

This facade was discussed in the first lecture of the series describing the importance and use of perspective. Turner's lecture referred to the debate then raging at the Royal Academy about the comparative merits of geometric elevations and perspective drawings. It had become common practice to draw geometric elevations with shadows added, a habit despised by Turner who strongly preferred fully realised perspective diagrams. As a companion to this rather flat geometric elevation with its added shadows, Turner also produced a more elaborate perspective view of the Admiralty (T.B. CXCV 173).

25 **Interior of a Prison** *c.*1810
pen and ink and watercolour 710 × 510
(28 × 20)
Turner Bequest; CXCV 128
D17099

This sheet is one of a small group of studies (see also T.B. CXCV 120 and 121), based on an etching of Piranesi, pl.2 of the *Prima parte di Architettura e Prospettive* of 1743.

Turner had studied Piranesi's work in the collection of Sir Richard Colt Hoare, an early patron, and Piranesi's magnificent architectural fantasies played a large part in forming Turner's style as an artist of the architectural sublime.

Even in this developed perspective study, Turner manages to convey a sense of slightly sinister gloom.

26 **An Ionic Capital of a Pillar** *c.*1810
pencil and watercolour 673 × 1005
(26½ × 39½)
Turner Bequest; CXCV 125
D17096

This drawing, along with the 'Interior of a Prison' (cat.no.25), and 'Brocklesby Mausoleum' (cat.no.21), forms part of a group in which Turner is concerned with the effects of shadows on objects, a topic largely derived from Thomas Malton's *Complete Treatise on Perspective* of 1775.

In a poem in one of his sketchbooks Turner refers to the Orders of Architecture; the Tuscan order he describes as a 'Labourer' and the Corinthian he characterises as 'mature of grace'. The ram-horned Ionic he describes as follows:

Ionic with her scrowl like fan
The meretricious courtezan
It now is used at front of Houses
To shew those horns belong to spouses ...

27 **Part of Trajan's Column** *c.*1810
pencil and watercolour 980 × 642
(38½ × 25¼)
Turner Bequest; CXCV 153
D17124

This beautiful drawing illustrates a section of Trajan's Column in Rome and was used in the introductory perspective lecture along with 'St George's, Bloomsbury' (cat.no.23).

Turner discussed the distortion of the proportions of buildings in elevation and referred to the long-standing debate as to whether the spirals on Trajan's Column were larger at the top than at the bottom.

28 **Classical Columns** *c.*1810
pen and ink, pencil and watercolour
583 × 714 (23 × 28⅛)
Turner Bequest; CXCV 171
D17142

In the Perspective Lectures Turner drew repeatedly on Stuart and Revett's *Antiquities of Athens* (1810), although he criticised their use of geometric elevations. This diagram was used to show the failings of such elevations; Turner produced two drawings of this colonnade, one in a simple pen and ink outline, and this watercolour. The ink drawing is difficult to read, but the use of shadows in the watercolour creates a sense of depth so that the respective positions of the columns can be seen.

29 **Rome: the Arch of Constantine and the Colosseum** 1819
pencil and watercolour 233 × 370
(9⅛ × 14½)
Turner Bequest; CLXXXIX 29
D16355

Turner's first visit to Italy gave rise to a large quantity of careful records of scenery and architecture capturing the spirit of Italy, both ancient and modern. In Rome, he surveyed the townscape as a whole and also studied specific buildings in great detail.

This beautifully observed pencil drawing manages to convey all the grandeur and magnificence of ancient Rome on a small scale. The placing of the arch diagonally to the picture plane, reaching up to the corner of the sheet, is a device borrowed from Piranesi, whose etchings in the *Vedute di Roma* Turner would have seen in the collection of Sir Richard Colt Hoare, an early patron.

30 **Rome: the Colosseum** 1819
pencil, watercolour and bodycolour 231 × 369
(9 × 14½)
Turner Bequest; CLXXXIX 37
D16364

The individual buildings which Turner studied in Rome were usually monuments of great size and historical significance, such as the Colosseum, which was a particularly poignant reminder to the tourist of what Rome had been.

In this drawing, the grandeur of the Colosseum was not subordinated to the effects of climate or atmosphere; this is simply a precise record of the structure of the building. Turner drew the Colosseum many times on this visit to Rome, selecting different viewpoints so as to record the maximum amount of material. A finished watercolour of the Colosseum, showing the building from the opposite side and in a more picturesquely dramatic vein, is in the British Museum (Lloyd Bequest).

31 **The Portico of St Peter's, Rome** 1819
pencil, watercolour and bodycolour
368 × 232 (14½ × 9⅛)
Turner Bequest; CLXXXIX 6
D16332

It must have been difficult for Turner on his first visit to Rome not to see the city through the eyes of other artists, but in general, his view of it was remarkably spontaneous and fresh.

Although the grandiose scale of this drawing is reminiscent of Piranesi, the vision is entirely original, a personal response to the architecture of St Peter's. The scale of Michelangelo's portico is greatly exaggerated by the tiny figure beside it, continuing the tradition of the architectural sublime that Turner had followed in the 1790s. Unlike the large drawing of 'Ely Cathedral' (cat.no.7), this watercolour achieves its effect on a smaller sheet of paper, largely through understatement.

32

32 **East Cowes Castle: the Terrace from the West** 1827
pen and ink, with chalk 140 × 190 (5½ × 7½)
Turner Bequest; CCXXVII(a) 3
D20806

During the late 1820s, Turner made numerous drawings on small sheets of blue paper most often using watercolour and bodycolour. As well as the famous Petworth and 'French Rivers' series there are a large number of sketches associated with East Cowes Castle. This was the home of the architect John Nash (1752–1835), who designed and built it himself. Turner's use of pen and ink in this study conveys economically the architectural form of the castle, only vaguely suggesting the crenellated details of the towers. During the visit of 1827 Turner also produced several paintings of the Regatta at Cowes in which the castle appears (Gallery 102).

33 **East Cowes Castle; a Vaulted Passage** 1827
pen and ink with chalk 191 × 140 (7½ × 5½)
Turner Bequest; CCXXVII(a) 10
D20813

East Cowes Castle was built by the architect John Nash in 1798. Unfortunately the Castle was destroyed so that Turner's drawings constitute an almost unique record of the building as it was when Nash was living there. This drawing seems not to depict an interior of the castle, but perhaps shows the entrance to some kind of garden folly with the added decorations of an urn and a bust. Nash was a popular architect in his lifetime, especially with George IV for whom he built the Royal Pavilion at Brighton.

34

34 Rouen: La Rue de la Grosse Horloge
*c.*1832
pen and ink, watercolour and bodycolour
142 × 192 (5½ × 7½)
Turner Bequest; CCLIX 257
D24822

Turner visited Rouen while collecting material
for a series of engravings of views of the Seine
published under the title *Turner's Annual Tour*.
For this project Turner made studies of the many
types of buildings he saw on his travels including
chateaux, hotels, and cathedrals. In this drawing
the vernacular architecture of the town is con-
trasted with the looming spires of the cathedral.
The great clock-tower which dominates the street
was built in 1527, although the actual clock dates
back to 1389.

35 The West Front of Rouen Cathedral
*c.*1832
pen and ink, with watercolour and
bodycolour 140 × 194 (5½ × 7⅝)
Turner Bequest; CCLIX 109
D24674

Turner made a preparatory sketch of the west
front of Rouen Cathedral in his *Dieppe, Rouen and
Paris* sketchbook (cat.no.55). This drawing was
engraved as part of Turner's series of views on
the River Seine which he published in 1834. The
wide expanse of the Gothic facade rises up beyond
the limits of Turner's small sheet of paper, and
even the arch on the left-hand side of the drawing
is insufficient to frame its immensity. This effect is
also heightened by the cluster of buildings at the
base of the cathedral and the swirl of ant-like

humanity. In contrast to the intricacy of his
sketchbook drawing, Turner's rendering of the
profusely carved facade is here an excuse for a
study of the reflected light on the cathedral.
Claude Monet was later to make similar studies of
the same effect on this building.

36 A Gothic Screen, Rouen *c.*1832
pen and ink, with watercolour and
bodycolour 140 × 193 (5½ × 7½)
Turner Bequest; CCLIX 149
D24714

This Gothic Screen, situated near the cathedral,
with its ogee-headed arches was first noted by
Turner in the *Dieppe, Rouen, Paris* sketchbook
(T.B. CCLVIII 10). As in the earlier watercolour
of 'Durham' (cat.no.14), Turner adopts a low
angle from which he delineates the intricate
sculpture of the screen as well as the cathedral
buildings seen through its arches. Along with the
drawing of 'La Rue de la Grosse Horloge', this
drawing was probably made more for Turner's
own pleasure than for the possibility of its inclusion in his engraved views of the Seine.

37 The Louvre; the Grande Galerie 1821
pencil with chalk 123 × 185 (4⅞ × 7¼)
Turner Bequest; CCLX 88
D24924

Turner had visited the Louvre after the Treaty of
Amiens on his first visit to the Continent in 1802.
Although Napolean had managed to assemble a
huge collection of some of the finest works of art in
Europe, there were many complaints that the bad
lighting in the gallery made it impossible to see
the paintings. However, a system of top-lighting
which had been proposed for a number of years
was installed by 1821 when Turner revisited
Paris. He made notes of the gallery in the *Loire,
Tours, Orleans, and Paris* sketchbook (T.B. CCXLIX
43a) as well as two other studies of this sort on
blue paper (T.B. CCLX 90, 125). The top-
lighting was a feature in which Turner was particularly interested as he had devised a similar
system of lighting in his own picture gallery which
was then nearing completion, as well as intro-
ducing alterations in the lighting of the lecture
room at the Royal Academy in 1809.

38 Hotel de Ville, Louvain *c.*1834
pen and ink with watercolour and bodycolour
140 × 188 (5½ × 7⅜)
Turner Bequest; CCXXII D
D20263

Turner visited the Belgian city of Louvain (now Leuven) in 1834. Like the watercolour and bodycolour studies made to illustrate his journeys on the Loire and the Seine, Turner produced many drawings of the scenery of the Rivers Meuse and Moselle. He had conceived the idea of a 'Rivers of Europe' project for which he perhaps intended to use this subject. Turner made studies of Louvain in the *Spa Dinant and Namur* sketchbook (T.B. CCLXXXVII) as well as another study in pen and bodycolour (T.B. CCLIX 25). In these sketches Turner contrasts the florid late-Gothic style of the Town Hall, dating from 1448–63, with the slightly more austere building of the church of St Pierre which was built earlier in the fifteenth century.

39

39 The Forum *c.*1827
pencil and watercolour 247 × 307 (9¾ × 12)
Turner Bequest; CCLXXX 158
D27675

This beautiful drawing and that of the 'Villa Madama' below, were commissioned by Samuel Rogers as illustrations for his long contemplative poem *Italy*, and were published in their engraved form in 1830. Turner contributed twenty-five designs of architectural and landscape subjects which, despite their small size, show a complete command of the architectural scale of the views and are as spacious and as richly inventive as Turner's largest paintings.

The design of the vignettes was perhaps influenced by Rogers's own interest in neo-Classical art, but they also relate to Turner's architectural interests of the time which can be seen in a comparison between this illustration and the painting 'Forum Romanum' (Gallery 104).

40 Villa Madama – Moonlight *c.*1827
pencil and watercolour 241 × 297
(9½ × 11⅜)
Turner Bequest; CCLXXX 159
D27676

Raphael, one of the principal architects of the Villa Madama, was an artist to whom Turner had already paid tribute in his painting 'Rome from the Vatican' (Gallery 104). This illustration accompanies the lines:

> This rising moon we hailed,
> Duly, devoutly, from a vestibule
> Of many an arch, o'er-wrought and lavishly
> With many a labyrinth of sylphs and flowers,
> When Raphael and his school from Florence
>   came,
> Filling the land with splendour …

41 Merton College, Oxford *c.*1835
watercolour 294 × 432 (11½ × 17)
Turner Bequest; CCLXIII 349
D25472

In the 1790s, Oxford had been particularly fashionable as a source of picturesque views. Turner, in his early years, had been especially attracted to the 'collegiate Gothick' architecture of Oxford and had made several views to be engraved for the Oxford Almanack. The churches, colleges and bridges of Oxford continued to hold sway over his imagination, though to a lesser degree, later in his career. This watercolour, from the 1830s, was apparently intended as a design for the series of topographical prints 'Picturesque Views in England and Wales', but was never engraved.

A sketchbook showing what is perhaps a preliminary study for this watercolour of Merton College is also displayed (cat.no.56).

42 The Campanile of St Mark's with the Pilastri Acritani from the Porta della Carta 1840
pencil, watercolour and bodycolour
282 × 191 (11⅛ × 7½)
Turner Bequest; CCCXVII 19
D32204

Turner visited Venice at least three times and the impression that the city had on him resulted in an enormous output of work in both watercolour and oil. Turner was struck by the sheer beauty of the city as well as the unending combinations of shapes which its varied buildings presented to the eye.

This watercolour is an important example of how Turner's architectural observations can help with scholarly analysis of his work; most of the Venetian watercolours have been difficult to date, but here he has shown the Campanile covered with scaffolding, a feature which was known to have been in place in 1840. This and other related drawings can therefore be dated to Turner's last visit to Venice.

43 The Casa Grimani and Rio S. Luca on the Grand Canal 1840?
pencil and watercolour 221 × 324
(8¾ × 12¾)
Turner Bequest; CCCXV 7
D32123

The roll sketchbook from which this study comes contains several studies of buildings along the Grand Canal which seem to have been made with the intention of recording the architecture as much as conveying the atmosphere of the city.

Turner has clearly delineated the recession of the buildings as they follow the Grand Canal adding sufficient details for his purposes but has obviously found interesting the atmospheric effects of buildings as they merge into their reflections.

44 Ponte della Guerra with the Palazzo Tasca-Papafava beyond 1840
pencil, watercolour and bodycolour
194 × 279 (7⅝ × 11)
Turner Bequest; CCCXVII 30
D32215

A number of the Venetian watercolours on grey paper (see cat.no.42) have a strongly topographical character, paying great attention to architectural details, and with compositions often enclosed by architectural forms. In this watercolour Turner has moved away from the open vistas of the Grand Canal to a more mysterious and maze-like area of Venice. However these are still buildings of historic and artistic interest: they include the Palazzo Tasca-Papafava with its elegant Renaissance doorway and the Ponte della Guerra, the scene of street brawls between rival Venetian families in the Middle Ages.

45 The Ducal Palace: the Porta della Carta 1833
pencil, watercolour and bodycolour
305 × 234 (12 × 9¼)
Turner Bequest; CCCXVIII 28
D32247

It was not until the 1830s that Turner showed an interest in Venetian architecture other than those classical buildings by Palladio, Sansovino or other Renaissance masters for which Venice was famous.

Turner's depiction of the Porta della Carta, however, is a composition consisting entirely of Byzantine and Gothic buildings which are rendered with a sure understanding of their structure. The use of brown paper was perhaps more conducive to the depiction of the more sombre architectural styles of Romanesque or Gothic and for single architectural features or interiors. This watercolour perhaps most nearly anticipates Ruskin's views of Venetian architecture later to be published in his *Stones of Venice* in 1851.

46 Fribourg 1841
pencil with pen and ink and watercolour
234 × 338 (9¼ × 13⅜)
Turner Bequest; CCCXXXV 18
D33558

In many of his late Swiss subjects Turner draws the outlines of his chosen view with a pen dipped in ink or watercolour, often apparently as a means of delineating complex architectural subjects in the short time his visits allowed. He passed through the Swiss town of Fribourg on his tour of

1841. As well as a group of watercolours showing the spectacular view from the suspension bridge at Fribourg, Turner made a detailed pencil drawing of the tall episcopal cathedral of St Nicholas so prominent in this view (T.B. CCCXXXV 2). On his first visit to Switzerland in 1802 Turner had complained of the style of Swiss houses: 'bad forms, – tiles abominable red colour'. The unusually shaped roofs and towers he discovered on his return, however, form a characteristic feature of these townscapes.

47 **Bellinzona** 1842–3
pencil and watercolour 227 × 335 (9 × 13⅛)
Turner Bequest; CCCXXXVI 16
D33595

Turner's late Swiss watercolours tend to be more concerned with landscape than with architecture; he often seems to fuse the buildings he includes into the washes evoking their surroundings. In this watercolour Turner concentrates on the Italianate church of SS Pietro e Stefano in the central piazza of Bellinzona. Although this is rendered in considerable detail, the emphasis of the drawing falls on the massive form of the Castello Grande, one of three garrisons near the city. Turner allows this to glow distinct from its surrounding with no suggestion of its darker uses as a prison and arsenal.

48 **Inside the Cathedral at Eu** 1845
pencil and watercolour 326 × 232
(12⅞ × 9⅛)
Turner Bequest; CCCLIX 10
D35445

The cathedral at Eu was founded during the eleventh century, but various building works went on until 1230. The cathedral was particularly notable for the curious double arches between the pillars of the nave, an effect Turner has tried to capture in this and another broadly handled watercolour study of the interior (T.B. CCCLIX 7).

49 **Eu: the Cathedral from the East** 1845
pencil and watercolour 232 × 326
(9⅛ × 12⅞)
Turner Bequest; CCCXXXIV 16
D33540

In this drawing Turner accentuates the scale of the cathedral by the inclusion of the group of figures dwarfed by its height. He was in Eu in 1845 and visited Louis Philippe at the chateau seen in the distance. The two men had become acquainted at Twickenham in 1815 when Turner lived at Sandycombe Lodge. The chateau seen here was the favourite residence of Louis Philippe, who was responsible for many alterations to the original sixteenth century building. Queen Victoria visited it on two occasions, in 1843 and 1845, and it is possible that Turner's visit coincided with the second of these.

50 **Eu: the Cathedral from the East** 1845
pencil and watercolour 232 × 328 (9⅛ × 13)
Turner Bequest; CCCLIX 16
D35451

John Ruskin wrote warmly of the architecture of the cathedral at Eu revealing the attractions Turner must have found in it: 'The apse of Eu is one of the most interesting in France in its bold pyramidal structure, being surrounded by a double range of chapels, with corresponding pinnacles and double flying buttresses'. He suggests that Turner made this watercolour 'by moonlight, in the sea fog'. The towering height of the building is shown from a similar low viewpoint to the drawings Turner made in his youth under the influence of Thomas Malton.

51 *North of England* sketchbook 1797
Lindisfarne: the Priory Church
pencil and sepia wash 270 × 209 (10⅝ × 8¼)
Turner Bequest; XXXIV 50
D00958

This is one of a group of studies in this sketchbook depicting the ruined Romanesque Priory Church of Lindisfarne. Like the *Tweed and Lakes* sketchbook also used on this tour, the book contains many architectural subjects.

52 Studies of the Organ Screen, York Minster *c.*1797–8
pencil 63 × 95 (2½ × 3¾), 95 × 63 (3¾ × 2½)
Turner Bequest; LI E, LI F
D02372, D02373

These two cards are good examples of Turner's fastidious draughtsmanship and observation of even the minutest architectural details. The sculptural figures of English Kings which are set in niches in the organ screen and the carved mouldings and details of the panelling are so precisely rendered as to enable him to reproduce the images exactly if the need arose.

These drawings were apparently executed during the North of England tour which Turner made in 1797.

53 *Raby* sketchbook 1817
Streatlam Castle, Staindrop
pencil 232 × 330 (9⅛ × 13)
Turner Bequest; CLVI 30 verso, 31
D12313, D12314

Other drawings in this sketchbook relate to commissioned pictures of Raby Castle and Gibside. It is possible therefore that this hightly finished drawing was made for a similar purpose. Turner has very carefully divided the left-hand page with the finest of pencil lines, beyond which he studies the component architectural features of cornice, windows, and cupola. The castle was much altered in 1841–2 by John and Benjamin Green and three new cupolas replaced the two wooden ones seen here. The castle was demolished in 1922.

54 *Hastings* sketchbook *c.*1815
Rosehill, Sussex
pencil 127 × 203 (5 × 8)
Turner Bequest; CXXXIX 33 verso, 34
D10392, D10393

Turner made several watercolours of Sussex for the M.P. Jack Fuller, the owner of Rosehill (now called Brightling Park). This elevation has been annotated by a sketch of the oriel window and a written comment serving as a reminder of the slightly obscured Ionic porch at the front of the house.

55 *Dieppe, Rouen and Paris* sketchbook 1821
The West Front of Rouen Cathedral
pencil 117 × 216 (4⅝ × 8½)
Turner Bequest; CCLVIII 21 verso, 22
D24540, D24541

This sketchbook contains many studies of the architecture of Rouen and its cathedral. The drawing on the right-hand page shows the west front and relates to a preparatory study for the engraved view of the cathedral Turner's technique here is reminiscent of the elegant style of his detailed adolescent architectural studies, such as the drawings of 'Ely' and 'Salisbury'.

56 *Oxford* sketchbook *c.*1834
Merton College
pencil 149 × 232 (5⅞ × 9⅛)
Turner Bequest; CCLXXXV 23 verso, 24
D27929, D27930

This drawing appears to be a study for the finished watercolour 'Merton College, Oxford' (cat.no.41). The surrounding details and annotations show Turner's intention to reproduce exactly those buildings which were the object of his study.

This sketchbook, produced some forty years after Turner's first visit to the city, contains several detailed views of Oxford colleges and churches; proof of Turner's abiding affection for Oxford's 'venerable assemblage of Gothic buildings'.

57 *Genoa and Florence* sketchbook 1828
The Duomo and Campanile, Pisa
pencil 146 × 98 (5¾ × 3⅞)
Turner Bequest; CCXXXIII 59 verso, 60
D21527, D21528

Like most visitors to Pisa, Turner was apparently captivated by the precarious tilt of the cathedral bell-tower. This sketch seems to place the tower at an even greater slant than usual and Turner draws the details of the tower accommodated to this angle.

Venice: The Piazzetta
pencil 111 × 190 (4⅜ × 7½)
Turner Bequest; CLXXV 42 verso, 43
D14394, D14395

This sketchbook from Turner's first visit to Venice seems to have been filled on one journey along the Grand Canal, sketching as he went and occasionally going ashore. This view in the Piazzetta di San Marco looking towards Sansovino's Library and the Campanile would have been as popular with tourists then, as it is today.

Turner has avoided sketching repetitive architectural featues by writing '24' on the arches of the Library and drawing only a few of them carefully. He has nevertheless noted unusual and interesting points of detail, annotating them with descriptions such as '... with gold stars'.

The Artist as Architect

Although Turner's frequently quoted remark, 'if I could have my time over again I would be an architect'[1], suggests an air of frustrated ambition, Turner did, in fact, complete three building projects. 'Consider the pleasure of being your own architect'[2] he wrote to his friend, James Holworthy, conveying something of the enthusiasm with which he must have pursued the construction of his own buildings.

No doubt Turner's early architectural training provided him with the essential skills to set about the process of design, and indeed his sketchbooks show that he followed the traditional practice of draughtsmen such as Thomas Malton or Thomas Hardwick in making detailed architectural elevations showing the proposed building in its landscape setting.

The first completed building was a villa for himself at Twickenham, for which he bought a plot of land at 'Sand pit close' in 1807. The house, however, was probably not completed until 1813 when Turner began to pay rates on it. Although Turner originally called the house 'Solus' Lodge, suggesting he viewed it as something of a retreat, it came to be known as Sandycombe Lodge, probably because of the sandy hollow on which it was built.

Turner made two basic designs for the house which he seems to have had some difficulty in reconciling. However, the completed building, as seen in a watercolour by William Havell, shows that Turner was able to integrate elements of both ideas. Despite this attention to the appearance of the outside of the house, Turner appears to have made no sketches of the proposed interior. Only one sketch shows any of the fittings, that of a fireplace which relates to the one still in the 'studio' at Sandycombe Lodge.

The house, with its mixture of 'rustic' and Palladian features, was not strikingly original as a design. It resembles the villas of contemporary pattern-books as well as containing details reminiscent of Sir John Soane's Pitshanger Manor, situated in nearby Ealing.

Although Turner complained that the house was 'an act of folly'[3] in view of his repeated absences on sketching tours, he lived there with his father until 1826 when Sandycombe was sold.

Turner was also involved with various architectural projects at Farnley Hall, the Yorkshire home of his friend Walter Fawkes. The most substantial was the gatehouse Turner apparently designed. A sketchbook of *c.*1817 shows the gates in an elevation of considerable detail.

Of Turner's buildings the most significant must surely be his Gallery where his architectural skills were utilised for the most effective display of his own art. He had chosen to exhibit away from the Royal Academy at his own Harley Street gallery in 1804. By 1810 he was considering building a new gallery to replace what he referred to as his 'Alladins palace'. His calculations of that year allowed £1,200 for the house and gallery which was eventually built at 47 Queen Anne Street, around the corner from the old gallery. Building work, however, did not begin until 1819 and the gallery was not to open until 1822. Turner paid considerable attention to the arrangements of the gallery, but he was also meticulous about such details as the front porch which he is alleged to have designed.

His decision to build a new gallery was doubtless reinforced by the opening of Sir John Soane's Dulwich Picture Gallery in 1811, and it is possible that Turner may have consulted Soane with regard to his own project. Turner was clearly anxious to provide a sympathetic architectural setting for his pictures. He observed to his fellow-painter C.R. Leslie that 'painting can never show her nose in company with architecture but to have it snubbed'.[4]

The picture 'Rome from the Vatican', was exhibited in 1820 whilst work was still under way on Turner's gallery, perhaps best exemplifies Turner's higher aims for his art. In the painting Raphael stands surrounded by his double achievement in art and architecture. Like Raphael, Turner compels us to admire a man who clearly had the potential to be 'great in any and everything he chose to take up'.[5]

[1] Walter Thornbury, *Life and Correspondence of J.M.W. Turner*, 1856, Vol.II, p.57; Patrick Youngblood, 'The Painter as Architect: Turner and Sandycombe Lodge, *Turner Studies*, Vol.2, no.1, p.23
[2] John Gage, *The Collected Correspondence of J.M.W. Turner*, Oxford 1980, Letter no.122, p.96
[3] Ibid, Letter no.56, pp.60–1
[4] C.R. Leslie, *Autobiographical Recollections*, EP Publishing Ltd 1978, Vol.I, p.208
[5] Walter Thornbury, *Life and Correspondence of J.M.W. Turner*, 2nd ed. 1877, p.236

WILLIAM HAVELL

59 **Sandycombe Lodge** 1814
pencil and watercolour
Private Collection

William Havell's drawing, made for Cooke's engravings of *Thames Scenery* (1814), shows the house soon after its completion. Turner has introduced a Doric triglyph motif on the wings of the house and on the central bay. This may be something he had borrowed from the new extension to Walter Fawkes's home at Farnley Hall. The River Thames is visible in the distance, clearly a picturesque device on Havell's part, along with two peacocks in the left-hand corner. Havell perhaps omitted these at Turner's request in the engraving based on this subject where they are noticeably absent.

60 **Sandycombe Lodge**
photograph

Sandycombe Lodge seems to have undergone structural alterations soon after Turner sold it in 1826 including the introduction of a second storey on either side of the main bay. The Doric triglyph motif visible in William Havell's watercolour of the house (cat.no.59), is no longer evident on the central part of the house, although it can still be seen on the corners of each wing. The photograph also shows the lunette window in the basement which is perhaps the nearest the house comes to resembling Pope's Twickenham villa, which Turner had depicted in its dilapidated state for the Royal Academy exhibition of 1808. During the last war Sandycombe was considerably damaged whilst used as a factory.

GEORGE JONES
61 **Lady Visitors in Turner's Gallery**
photograph; original painting in the
Ashmolean Museum, Oxford

Ruskin's father claimed that 'Nothing since Pompeii so impressed me as the interior of Turner's house'. Other visitors to the Gallery in Queen Anne Street record that they were initially led into the 'comparative dungeon' of Turner's dining-room before being allowed to proceed upstairs to the lightness of his Gallery. The red walls of George Jones's picture confirm the Rev. William Kingsley's claim: 'I am glad to be able to say what was the colour of the walls of Turner's gallery, and it was Indian Red, neither pale nor dark'. This second gallery was smaller than that in Harley street which had measured some 70 by 20 feet, but was improved by the addition of top-lighting, for which Turner made many detailed diagrams in the *Tabley* sketchbook (cat.no.65).

62 **Turner's House and Gallery,**
47 Queen Anne Street West
photograph

Turner closed his first gallery at number 64 Harley Street (now number 35) in 1816. He was largely responsible for the design of the new house at number 47 (now 23) Queen Anne Street, for which work began in 1819. One biographer suggests that Turner designed the doorway and Turner's friend George Jones records that it was 'the best architecture in the street'. The arched windows seen on either side of the doorway in the photograph, however, were added after Turner's time. The exterior of the house was largely dictated by the Duke of Portand, Turner's landlord, who stipulated that 'the front wall ... is to be built with new picked Stocks neatly pointed, it is not to be stuccoed'. Turner introduced only two windows on each floor of the thirty-five foot wide facade possibly as a means of evading window tax which was enforced until his death. The two north-facing windows on the first floor were those of Turner's studio which doubtless provided a suitable light for painting. The building was destroyed after the war in 1948.

63 *Farnley* sketchbook 1818
The East Lodge Gates, Farnley Hall
pencil 111 × 190 (4⅜ × 7½)
Turner Bequest; CLIII 13 verso, 14
D12017, D12018

The building shown on the right-hand page of this opening depicts the Lodge Gates which Turner built at the Yorkshire home of his friend, Walter Fawkes. Details on the opposite page transcribe particular features of the design, including the chimney, the window sill, and the construction of the gates themselves. Although Ruskin's wife Effie felt that the gatehouse was 'not quite a success', the elegant Greek design was obviously constructed to complement the existing building at Farnley, which had been added to in 1790 by Carr of York. Turner has noted the house in the background of the sketch and in the margin of the left-hand page.

64 *Guards* sketchbook c.1818
A groundplan of 47 Queen Anne Street West
pencil 67 × 95 (2⅝ × 3¾)
Turner Bequest; CLXIV 60 verso, 61
D13319, D13320

This drawing shows the ground floor of the House in Queen Anne Street below Turner's gallery. Turner apparently kept many of his best pictures in the dining-room (the large room at the front of the house), and his many unfinished works filled the room beyond.

65 *Tabley No.3* sketchbook 1808
Designs for top-lighting
pencil 108 × 184 (4¼ × 7¼)
Turner Bequest; CV 43 verso, 44
D07045, D07046

Turner seems to have been particularly concerned about the lighting conditions in his Queen Anne Street gallery. Several pages in this sketchbook show details of the top-lighting he proposed to introduce. He also notes the protective blinds used in the picture gallery at Tabley House, the seat of his patron Sir John Leicester. At Queen Anne Street Turner suspended a herring-net under the top-lights to produce a diffused light. Such an imaginative feature was obviously worthwhile, for the Rev. William Kingsley commented that it 'was the best lighted gallery I have ever seen'.

66 *Windmill and Lock* sketchbook c.1810–11
Designs for Sandycombe Lodge
pen and ink 86 × 114 (3⅜ × 4½)
Turner Bequest; CXIV 77 verso, 78
D08065, D08066

One of several pages which shows the proposed design for Sandycombe Lodge. Here the house is built out over the slope, which forms part of the site, with a lower arcaded-basement. Other pages in the sketchbook show a quite different design without the extending room at the back.

67 *Sandycombe and Yorkshire* sketchbook c.1810–11
Designs for Sandycombe Lodge
pencil 124 × 200 (4⅞ × 7⅞)
Turner Bequest; CXXVII 13 verso, 15
D08982, D08985

These pages represent an almost final stage in Turner's design of Sandycombe Lodge. The central bay is heightened, and the designs suggest the chamfered roofs built on the two wings.